PRAYER
Journal

PRAYER JOURNAL
@Copyright 2021 by **CHERONDA L. HESTER**
All rights reserved. No part of this book may be reproduced or transmitted in any form or by any means without prior written permission from the author.

ISBN: **978-1-953638-19-9**
LIBRARY OF CONGRESS CONTROL NUMBER
2021921194

Printed in the United States of America
This book or parts thereof may not be reproduced in any form, stored in a retrieval system, or transmitted in any form by any means-electronic, mechanical, photocopy, recording, or otherwise-without prior written permission of the publisher, except as provided by United States of America copyright law.

PUBLISHER
TA MEDIA & PRODUCTIONS LLC
DALLAS, TX 75240
WWW.PUBLISHYOURBOOKTODAY.INFO
WWW.TAMEDIACO.COM

Unless otherwise noted,
all Scripture quotations are taken from the
Holy Bible, New Living Translation
(PUBLIC DOMAIN PER BIBLEGATEWAY.COM)

GOD,

I have confidence that if I ask anything in Your name, according to Your will and in agreement with Your plan that You listen and You hear me according to 1 John 5:14

INTRODUCTION

Push Power Boss Prayer Journal is a tool to help you pray effectively. It will also help you track how and when God is answering your prayers. This prayer journal was created from my personal experience of trusting God to answer my prayers, writing, and tracking what I was believing God for and praising Him when it was fulfilled this is the journey, I share with you.

As a believer, you've been given the keys of the Kingdom (Matthew16:19). It's a must for you to know and operate in authority. Remember Jesus gave the disciples power and authority over the enemy according to Matthew 10:1. As a believer, you have that same power and authority, and you are seated with Christ. So, use the authority you've been given through prayer and confession.

Do you want to see change in your life? Are you believing God for change in the lives of your family members, children, or friends? Do you have a desire to see God answer prayers concerning your health, finances, your local community, city, state, or the world as a whole? I believe this journal will be a great asset to you as you embark on a journey of prayer and intercession. Watch God answer prayers as you decree over yourself and your family. It is my prayer that this tool is a blessing and helps increase your prayer life.

Remember, prayer is your answer. Perhaps you have been longing for change and wonder if God hears you. You may be wondering if you are really saved. This journal is also designed for you, and we can pray the pray of salvation together. Remember, according to Romans 10:9 "if you confess with your mouth that Jesus is Lord and believe in your heart that God raised Him from the dead, you'll be saved." Today, if you believe in your heart and confess with your mouth that Jesus is Lord, you are saved. Let's make a decision today to say the prayer of confession on the next page and embark on the journey of God. Once you read the prayer, all your sins are forgiven, and your past no longer holds you captive. Let me welcome you to the family as you embrace a life of prayer.

PRAYER OF SALVATION

Lord, I come to You now.
I acknowledge You as Lord Creator of heaven and earth. I confess that I am a sinner. I have sinned against You. I believe in my heart that Jesus Christ is Your Son, and You sent Your Son to die on the cross for me as a sacrifice for my sins. I believe in my heart that You raised Jesus from the dead and that He is alive today. Now, I repent (turning) from my sins and choosing to follow and obey Jesus Christ as my Lord and Savior with all my heart and believe that You are my Lord and my God. Come into my life as my Lord and Savior. Fill me with your Holy Spirit, use my life as a willing vessel. I believe that I am saved!

Thank you, Lord, for my salvation by faith in
Jesus Christ and the truth of Your Word.
In Jesus Name Amen!

_____   _____
NAME   DATE

Congratulations

HEAVEN IS REJOICING

PRAYER

Prayer- (interacting/communicating with God) is a solemn request for helping or expression of thanks addressed to God.

Prayer is the expression of our inner spiritual needs. Through prayer, we can find the strength of spirit, guidance, wisdom, joy, and inner peace. Psalm 118:5-6, Psalm138:3, Isaiah 58:9-11, Philippians 4:6-7, 1Peter5:7.

Your prayer may be long or short, alone or in a group, silent or aloud, but it should be true communication with our Lord and Savior and not done for public recognition Matthew 6:5-8.

When praying it's important to believe (have faith) what you're praying even if it's small faith. The bible talks about pray, believe and receive Mark 11:24.

I encourage you to call upon the Lord!!! The bible tells us He will answer us before we even call on Him. While we are talking about our needs, He will go ahead and answer our prayers Isaiah 65:24. The Lord's ears are open to the prayers of the righteous 1Peter 3:12.

FORMS OF PRAYER

"A.C.T.S"
ADORATION & BLESSINGS
CONFESSION/REPENTANCE
THANKSGIVING & GRATITUDE
SUPPLICATION/PETITION
INTERCESSION
SPIRITUAL WARFARE

ADORATION

Adoration is respect, reverence, strong admiration, or devotion to God.

WHY IT IS IMPORTANT TO ADORE GOD?

When you adore God, you will experience the presence of God which results in limitless favor, encouragement, healing, deliverance, joy, provision, LOVE, wholeness, and more.

Adore Him because He's worthy and that
God takes pleasure in our praise.

CONFESSION

Confession is owning up to your wrong and telling it forthrightly to God. This is part of your reconciliation process.

REMEMBER

Proverbs 28:13 He who covers his transgressions will not prosper, but whoever confesses and forsakes them will obtain mercy. If we confess our sins, He is faithful and righteous to forgive us of our sins and cleanse us from all unrighteousness.

THANKSGIVING & GRADITUDE

Thanksgiving is the expression of gratitude, especially to God. Gratitude is the quality of being thankful, ready to show appreciation for, and return kindness. Gratitude helps us see God. It opens our spiritual eyes, draws us to God, and brings peace. The act of giving thanks; grateful acknowledgment of benefits or favors, especially to God.

Philippians 4:6-7 reads, Do not be anxious about anything, but in every situation, by prayer and petition, with thanksgiving, present your requests to God. And the peace of God, which transcends all understanding will guard your hearts and your minds in Christ Jesus.

Supplication is the action of asking or begging for something earnestly or humbly. It's also a form of prayer but considered as kneeling down and bending down and bending in which someone makes a humble petition or an entreaty God.

Matthew 7:7-8 Ask, and it shall be given you; seek, and you shall find; knock and it shall be opened to you. For everyone who asks receives; the one who seeks finds; and him that knocks it shall be opened.

Intercession is the action of intervening on behalf of another. Praying to God in heaven on the behalf of oneself or others.

SPIRITUAL WARFARE

Spiritual Warfare is the believer's way of fighting against the work of **Spiritual Warfare** on biblical belief. Spiritual Warfare is a common prayer for breakthrough. Warfare is done in many ways laying on of the hands, fasting with prayer, praise, and worship, and anointing with oil. One thing you must remember is the enemy comes to kill, steal, and destroy so when we are pursuing Christ,
he tries to accomplish all those
things.

Although encountering spiritual warfare may be difficult,
God uses it to grow us even closer to Him.

Ephesian 6:12 For we wrestle not against flesh and blood, but against principalities, against powers, against the rulers of the darkness of this world against spiritual wickedness in high places.

PRAYER
SCRIPTURES

date _____

daily scripture or gratitude quote

My Prayers

_____
_____
_____

Blessings, favor **+** answered prayers

**REJOICE ALWAYS,
PRAY CONTINUALLY,
GIVE THANKS IN ALL
CIRCUMSTANCES;
FOR THIS IS
GOD'S WILL FOR YOU IN
JESUS**

date _____

daily scripture or gratitude quote

My Prayers

Blessings, favor **+** answered prayers

> THIS IS THE CONFIDENCE WE HAVE IN APPROACHING GOD: THAT IF WE ASK ANYTHING ACCORDING TO HIS WILL, HE HEAR US.
>
> **1 JOHN 5:14**

date _____

daily scripture or gratitude quote

My Prayers

Blessings, favor + answered prayers

AND IF WE KNOW THAT HE HEARS US, WHATEVER WE ASK WE KNOW THAT WE HAVE WHAT WE ASKED OF HIM

1 JOHN 5:15

date _____

daily scripture or gratitude quote

My Prayers

Blessings, favor + answered prayers

If my people, who are called
by my name, will humble themselves and pray
and seek my face and turn from their wicked
ways, then I will hear from heaven, and I will
forgive their sin and will heal their land.

2 CHRONICLES 7:14

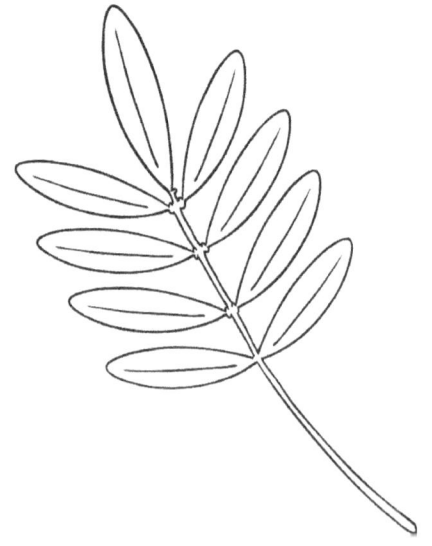

date _____

daily scripture or gratitude quote

My Prayers

Blessings, favor + answered prayers

> Then you will call on me and come and pray to me, and I will listen to you.
> **JEREMIAH 29:12**

date _____

daily scripture or gratitude quote

My Prayers

Blessings, favor + answered prayers

You will pray to him, and he will hear you, and you will fulfill your vows.

JOB 22:27

date _____

daily scripture or gratitude quote

My Prayers

Blessings, favor + answered prayers

Therefore I tell you,
whatever you ask for in prayer, believe
that you have received it,
and it will be yours.

MARK 11:24

date _____

daily scripture or gratitude quote

My Prayers

_____
_____
_____
_____

Blessings, favor + answered prayers

I call on you, my God,
for you will answer me; turn your ear to
me and hear my prayer.
PSALM 17:6
___

date _____

daily scripture or gratitude quote

My Prayers

Blessings, favor + answered prayers

Thou shalt also decree a thing, and it shall be established unto thee: and the light shall shine upon thy ways.
JOB 22:28

date _____

daily scripture or gratitude quote

My Prayers

Blessings, favor + answered prayers

Search for the Lord and for his strength; continually seek him.

CHRONICLES 16:11

www.ingramcontent.com/pod-product-compliance
Lightning Source LLC
Chambersburg PA
CBHW071201160426
43196CB00011B/2151